The First of Many Rescues

Meet Mickey!

First Edition
USA
Library of Congress Catalog Number: 2020924111

Publishing Services:
My iDeal Publishing
6237 Presidential Ct.
Suite 140
Fort Myers, FL 33919

ISBN 13: 978-1-9476789-3-4 (Hardcover)
ISBN 10: 1-947678-93-0 (Hardcover)

For ordering information please contact the publisher at:
ordering@happydolphinpress.com
www.HappyDolphinPress.com

Contact the author at www.FriendliesSeries.com

Ballerdy Books, LLC

Greetings, fellow dog lovers! My name is Mickey and I have a very special story to share. In fact, it's more like a tribute than a story. Yes, that's it! This is a tribute to me, a very special doggie that came into my forever mommy's life in an unexpected way. And so did the lives of many doggies for years to come.

The day I met my forever mommy is a day that I will always remember. Though it started off very sad and scary, it ended up being better than I could have ever expected. It's funny how things work out sometimes.

Well, this is my story...

My Mommy Cindy had been crying as she vacuumed. I knew it wasn't because of the vacuum; that was something she had done several times a week since I was a puppy! My brothers, Lukie and Max, shed as much as I did so she was always using that big ol' loud thing. It wasn't our fur that made her eyes water so much. It must have been all of the people who kept coming and going. I didn't like the people coming and going, either.

Thankfully, it was getting late in the day. There would be no more people coming to upset my Mommy Cindy. Or so I thought. When the doorbell rang, (again) a slender woman walked into our house. She was followed by an older woman. The two ladies did what everyone else had been doing. They walked up and down the hallways. They opened all of the closet doors. They even peered under the bed. I didn't know what they were looking for, but they searched and searched. They even opened up the cabinets in our kitchen. Were they hungry? Were they looking for a hidden treasure? If they were looking for a treasure, my precious chew toy would not be discovered! I grabbed it and snuck under the kitchen table. I was hoping they wouldn't see me or my chew toy.

The young woman began talking to my Mommy Cindy about the number of bedrooms in our house and how Mommy Cindy had recently redone her bathroom. Phew! They didn't seem to care about me or my chew toy….until this strange young woman pulled the table cloth up over the table, exposing my trembling body and my treasure. She looked at me straight in the face and asked, "Does this dog come with the house?"

Mommy Cindy began crying again and this time, she sat down with the strangers and began to tell the story of why she had been so sad lately. The news hit me like a ton of bricks. It was as if the kitchen table crashed down on me. Mommy Cindy tearfully explained that she was selling our home and that all of the people that had come in and out were interested in buying it. But that wasn't the reason why she was so sad. What I heard next was way worse than being hit with a ton of bricks or having a kitchen table crash down on me. She explained that she was moving to a small apartment and that my brothers, Max and Lukie, were going with her. My brother Max is a Min Pin and Lukie is a Chihuahua. Me, on the other hand, I am a Sheltie Collie. Apparently, Sheltie Collies are too big for small apartments. I understood why Max and Lukie had been sad, too. Everyone was moving but ME!

Mommy Cindy mumbled between the sobs, "If I can't find a new home for my beloved Mickey, I will have no choice but to take him to the shelter."

The slender stranger, Ann-Marie, burst into tears. Even though she didn't know me at that moment, she was sad, too!

"No! You can't take him to the shelter," she gasped. "Mickey can come live with me!"

Even though I didn't know Ann-Marie or the older woman that was with her, an overwhelming feeling of relief came over me. These people seemed really nice and Ann-Marie kept repeating how cute I am and how much she loved my eyes. She was cooing over me the same way that people do when they meet a brand new baby. If I couldn't go to the new home with Mommy Cindy and my brothers, at least I could have a place to live with Ann-Marie.

"Even though this isn't the house for me, I feel it in my heart that Mickey is the right dog for me," I heard Ann-Marie say.

Once again, the table cloth was lifted from the kitchen table and I could see the strangers staring right at me. Mommy Cindy reached for me. I quickly grabbed my favorite chew toy as she led me out from under the table and towards the front door. Mommy Cindy grabbed my favorite red leash that was hanging in its usual spot and clipped it to my collar. She slowly handed the leash to Ann-Marie. Tears fell from Cindy's eyes like a waterfall. She bent down beside me, wrapped her arms around my neck, and pressed her cheek against my face. As I had always done, I licked her cheeks and her neck but this time, she didn't wipe off the slobber with her sleeve. Instead, she placed her hand on her moist cheek, closed her eyes and cried.

"I love you Mickey. I will love you forever."

At that moment, she turned around, shoulders slumped and walked away. My brothers walked towards me, barking their last good-byes.

"Come on, Mickey," Ann-Marie said. "Let's go home."

That is a day that will be forever etched into my memory. Not only is it the last day that I spent with Mommy Cindy and my brothers, but it was a day that

changed my life. It changed Ann-Marie's life. And it changed the lives of other doggies for years to come.

It was a beautiful Autumn day. The leaves had begun to change colors. The crisp red and golden yellow leaves seemed to sparkle in the early morning sunshine. They danced in the cool breeze, as if to happily welcome the new season. I could feel the crisp, cool air blowing in from the open bedroom window. I was ready to play outside, but Ann-Marie had to go to work.

While Ann-Marie was at work teaching, I stayed inside, usually taking naps on our bed with The Friendlies as I waited for her to return home. I was different than some other dogs. And better, in my opinion. I didn't chew The Friendlies. I didn't bite off their ears or slobber on their faces. Unlike other dogs, I didn't tear open their bellies and feast on the fluffy cotton inside. Instead, I relaxed with them and enjoyed their company while Ann-Marie was educating children.

The hours passed slowly when Ann-Marie was gone, except when Grandma Jerrie came to visit. Every day

around noon, like clockwork, Grandma Jerrie came over to see me. No matter what the weather, we went outside to play! We had something in common. Both of us loved tennis! Grandma Jerrie played tennis like every other human does. She hit the tennis balls with a racquet. As for me, I just liked to play with the tennis balls. Grandma Jerrie would throw the balls across the backyard and I'd run like the wind, chasing after them. Sometimes, my squirrel friends would join in on the fun. They'd dash across the top of the fence, and up and down the trees. I'd bark and bark as I chased the tennis balls. It was so much fun!

Sometimes when I was playing with the squirrels, I would think about my brothers. They always enjoyed playing outside, too. I wondered what they were doing and if they liked their new apartment. I missed having those boys around to play with. I missed them terribly. It was like Grandma Jerrie could read my mind because that weekend, she set up a play date!

Saturdays and Sundays were my favorite days of the week. Ann-Marie didn't have to go to work, which meant I had company all day. On this particular weekend, we returned home to find a very special surprise waiting for us on the porch.

Grandma Jerrie's dearest friend, Sue, came over with her grand-doggie, Jordie. Like Max and Lukie, Jordie was a small dog. His soft hair was parted perfectly in the middle, as if someone had taken a comb and separated his hair into two perfect sections. Maybe his Mommy Danielle did that. After all, she was a hair dresser. Maybe she styled Jordie's hair just like she did with the humans.

My Mommy Cindy had always taught me to be kind to others. No matter their size, no matter their breed, no matter their color. She said it was important to show others kindness, especially because we don't know where those doggies had been or what kind of lives they had. Perhaps they had lived some of their short lives in shelters. Perhaps they had lived in houses with people that weren't very nice to them. No matter what, Mommy Cindy always taught me to be kind.

Things were no different when I met my new friend, Jordie. Of course, I was nice to him. It was easy to be nice to him. Jordie reminded me a lot of Max and Lukie because not only was he a small dog, too, but he was calm and gentle, just like my brothers.

My favorite thing about Jordie, though, was the way his tongue hung out of his mouth. It was like he was

always thirsty but I knew Auntie Sue and Danielle gave Jordie plenty of water because he told me so! Just like me, his humans took very, very good care of him.

When we walked inside, I followed Jordie around everywhere. When he found a comfortable spot on the couch, I hopped up on the couch and laid there, too.

When our humans were busy chatting, Jordie and I went outside to play. I introduced him to my squirrel friends and he seemed quite happy to meet them. While our humans were eating dinner, Jordie and I waited patiently together under the table, hoping that they would drop morsels of food on the floor. Even though we had already eaten our dinners, we enjoyed the extra snacks!

When he sat beside the pantry in our kitchen, probably hoping that his human would give him some people food, I sat there beside him, too. I just loved being in his company. Life is always better with friends.

"He is a really good dog," I heard Grandma Jerrie say. At first, I thought she was referring to my pal, Jordie. But then I realized she was talking about me!

"I feel so blessed to have found Mickey. He was already house broken. He was very well trained. He loves to sleep in and doesn't bother me in the morning to go outside. He actually wants to stay in bed longer than I do," Ann-Marie laughed.

I felt blessed, too. Being with Ann-Marie and her family was way better than moving to a shelter. Who knows where I would have ended up had she not rescued me! Besides, I am scared of strangers. Shelters are filled with strangers.

I was starting to meet more and more humans during my new life with my forever mommy. When Ann-Marie's teacher friends would come to visit, sometimes they would include me in their conversations! I'd sit right at the table, just like the humans did. I felt special and included.

Other times, when visitors came over, I was timid and shy. Ann-Marie's dad (my new Grandpa Joe) came over to our house quite a lot. He is very handy and knows how to fix things and build things. At first, when he came to the house, I was scared. He was another new face and I didn't trust him. Mommy Cindy's husband was as angry as he was tall. He was always yelling and saying mean things. I was worried that Grandpa Joe

may act like that, too, so when he visited, I kept my distance.

"I'd really like to pet him," Grandpa Joe said. (I think my eyes are irresistibly cute!)

"Just give him time," Ann-Marie said. "He'll warm up to you."

Then one day, I came to a conclusion. Grandpa Joe is nothing like Cindy's old husband. Grandpa Joe loves animals, especially doggies. He is a nice man. He is helpful, too. Whenever he came over to our house, he was there to help fix things. Maybe he would even fix my favorite chew toy. It was practically split in two. I decided at that moment that I was safe and that it would be okay to get close to him.

As I slowly walked over to Grandpa Joe, I dropped my chew toy by his feet. He smiled from ear to ear and said, "I think Mickey is ready for me to pet him now!"

I sure was! He outstretched his arm slowly and when he placed his hand on my head, I felt safe and loved. From that day forward, whenever Grandpa Joe was in our house, I was right beside him, wagging my tail and

waiting excitedly for more pats on the head! (When was he going to repair my chew toy?)

That day was like a turning point for me. After I felt more comfortable with Grandpa Joe, I visited him at *his* house, too! When Ann-Marie would announce that it was time to go see Grandma Jerrie and Grandpa Joe, I could hardly contain my excitement. I would jump up and down joyously, making it quite difficult for Ann-Marie to get my harness on. I would happily bark and bark. My barks echoed through the house.

There are other members of the family that I really loved, as well. My forever mommy has an older brother, Anthony and a twin sister named Teresa. Although Ann-Marie and Teresa look very much alike, I could tell them apart. You see, sometimes my Aunt Teresa would come over to let me outside. When my mommy was going to be out for too many hours, my Aunt Teresa would let me outside to do my business. (I am a very good boy. I never do poopies inside!) Well, the thing is, when I would hear the jiggling of the house key and the door knob, I would get really excited thinking that my mommy was finally home. I raced over to the front door and to my dismay, it wasn't my mommy. It was Aunt Teresa. Sure, I was happy to see her, too, but she wasn't my mommy.

"Oh, it's just you," I would bark. (I hope she couldn't understand me.)

My mommy and I had a very special bond. Not only did she save me from the dreaded shelter life, but she loved me like no other. I could feel it in my bones. It was different than the love that I had felt from Cindy or from my brothers. It was more powerful than any love I had ever known. She was my constant companion and friend. I just wanted to be with her all the time.

After a long day of being apart, I would ask, "Mom, where have you been all day, Mom? I hope that it's fun wherever you go because you're gone for an awful long time, Mom."

I was still waiting to find out what it was that she did all day. I knew she was at work and I knew she was a teacher, but what in the world took so long?

You know, I am a very smart doggie. I can almost tell time. Every night, I could sense when it was getting close to 9:00 pm. That was our bedtime. A little before 9, I would paw at Mommy. No matter what she was doing, I wanted her to stop. I would paw gently on her leg and then I'd walk down the long hallway that lead to our bedroom. After taking a few steps, I'd

pause and look back at my mommy. I wanted to make sure she was following me. I didn't have to say a thing. She knew what I was implying. It was time for bed.

It must have been my cute eyes that drew her in. I think she would have followed me anywhere, but the bed was one of her favorite places, too. She loved to cuddle with me and together, we always felt safe. I was certainly a bed hog! There was lots of room on our bed, but I had to be super close to my mommy. I don't think there was an inch of space between us! Sometimes, she would say, "Mickey, move over!" Nahhh.

The years had passed. The seasons changed from Spring to Summer to Fall to Winter eight times. I had a wonderful life with my forever family. Just when I thought things couldn't get any better, I heard some great news!

"Jen and Lola are coming to visit," Mommy announced.

Oh my goodness! I LOVED Lola! She was my little sweetheart! When the doorbell rang, I zoomed to the front door and let out my most welcoming bark. I wanted to jump like a kangaroo but my body was getting older and I just couldn't leap into the air like

I used to. That didn't matter. What mattered was that Lola was coming over to play! I followed Lola all around the house. Wherever she went, I trotted right behind her. I loved when Lola came to visit, especially after she had just finished at the groomer. She smelled so good! She tasted yummy, too! As she pranced around the house, showing off her new haircut, I'd sneak in a lick or two....or ten.

"Stop slobbering all over Lola," Jen would yell. "I just had her cleaned."

I know, I know. Her shampoo tastes so scrumptious! Jen would peer over at Ann-Marie with this serious look in her eyes, as if she was expecting my mommy to yell at me, too. But she didn't yell. She just laughed. Mommy knew how much I enjoyed Lola's company....and her sweet-tasting fur. It was like licking cotton candy! What she didn't know, though, was that Lola was my girlfriend!

Spending time with my mommy was my favorite thing to do. Playing tennis with Grandma Jerrie was also very enjoyable, but I wasn't able to do much of that anymore. My legs were getting weaker. Sometimes, it was even difficult for me to walk. It became more of a strain to climb up onto the bed, so I stayed on my blanket a lot.

"You look sad, my perfect Mickey. I think a visit with Grandma Mary will cheer you up," Ann-Marie announced cheerfully.

Mommy gently lifted me into the car. I loved going on car rides. I loved feeling the fresh air on my cute face.

This car ride was short. Grandma Mary lived around the corner! We used to walk over to see her, but walking had become quite painful for me.

When we arrived at Grandma Mary's, she greeted us at the door. She was always wearing a colorful hand-made house dress. Her hair was as white as the hair on my chest and paws. Her big smile was so welcoming. She sure did love company!

My mommy carried me inside. She placed me down on the wooden floor next to a full bowl of dog food that Grandma Mary had lovingly prepared. Like most Italian grandmas, this lovely lady always had delicious food to share! One thing Italian grandmas like to eat is cheese, so I wasn't surprised to find a generous portion of grated mozzarella cheese sprinkled on my snack. Thanks, Grandma Mary!

"You can stay here and keep me company while your mommy goes out," Grandma Mary said in a chipper voice. "I'm glad you're here. It sure is lonely around here sometimes."

After Grandma Mary's husband passed away, she felt very lonely. She had been married for over 56 years and was used to having a companion. She appreciated my company and welcomed me into her home with open arms....and lots of treats!

I think my mommy could tell that my body was growing older. I overheard her talking to my Grandma Jerrie one evening.

"I want to have a birthday party for Mickey," Ann-Marie announced. "I am not sure how much longer he will be here with us, and I want this birthday to be very special."

"Ok, I am happy to help," Grandma Jerrie said, encouraging Mommy's idea.

That weekend, my mommy carefully put my red harness on my aging body. She told me that we were going for a short walk and that she wanted to spend some time with me, just the two of us.

"If you get too tired, Mickey, we can turn around and come home."

Together, we walked slowly to Grandma Mary's house. When she happily answered the door, it seemed as though she wasn't expecting us.

"We are here to invite you to Mickey's birthday party," Ann-Marie announced gleefully, as she handed her the invitation to my party.

Grandma Mary accepted with a big smile and promised us that she would be there. We then headed over to Grandma Jerrie and Grandpa Joe's house, which was also nearby. Though my legs felt a little wobbly, I was very much enjoying this special time with my mommy. Besides, the day was perfect. The sun was shining. The breeze felt warm and refreshing. There was just something special about that day.

When we arrived at Grandma Jerrie and Grandpa Joe's, they invited us inside. Boy, was I glad to be there! I hadn't realized it before, but once we had stopped for a moment, I sure was tired! I plopped down on the living room floor and conked out. I bet I was even snoring! I am not sure how long I had dozed off for, but when I woke up, I heard Grandma Jerrie say, "We'll be there! Can't wait!"

At that point, I was just too exhausted to move. I wanted to stay there on the floor and just keep snoozing. I think my mommy could tell I needed a nap, so she let me have a sleepover! I *knew* there was something special about that day!

"I'll come back to pick him up in the morning," Ann-Marie promised.

The next day, Ann-Marie came bursting through the front door, holding three bright balloons. She ran right over to me, hugged me tightly and placed a kiss on my cheek.

"Happy Birthday, Perfect," she shouted. "It's time for your party!"

My party? Oh boy! A party just for me? I knew that Grandma Mary would be there. I knew that Grandpa Joe and Grandma Jerrie would be there. But would my pal, Jordie, be there, too? What about my girlfriend? Was she invited?

I did my best to get up as quickly as I could. I couldn't wait to get home and see who had come to my party!

When we walked through the door, I was amazed. Bright blue and red balloons were floating everywhere! Yellow streamers hung from the ceiling. Music was playing. There were even presents piled up on the table for me. As I made my way into the kitchen, I was overjoyed! Lola was there and so was Jordie! My furry friends had come to celebrate! They were even wearing party hats and I got to wear one, too! This was one of the best days of my life!

It became more and more challenging for me to get up and move around like I used to. Mommy and Grandma Jerrie took very good care of me. They didn't seem to mind that I couldn't move around as gracefully as I used to. I couldn't climb into the bathtub anymore, so when the weather was warm, my humans gave me a bath outside.

I never really liked baths. Ever. It was my least favorite thing to do. But my mommy always called me Perfect so I had to live up to my name. I didn't want to cause any trouble. Sometimes, instead of calling me by my actual name, she would refer to me as Perfect. If I made a fuss during bath time, I might lose my status! I patiently sat still and anxiously awaited my favorite part of bath time: being done!

Aside from being a perfect son during bath time, I am perfect in other ways, too. Mommy loved to give me hair cuts. I don't even think my hair grew back by the time she was ready to pull out the scissors again. But I figured if Jordie let his mommy cut his hair, I should let my mommy cut mine, too. When she was all done, she told me I am perfect and beautiful. I'm not beautiful, but my girlfriend, Lola, is.

My mommy treated me like a baby doll sometimes. She brushed my teeth. She dressed me up. One Spring day when she returned home from school, she told me that one of her students had given her an Easter present for me. When I saw what she had pulled out of her bag, I thought, "Are you kidding me? Are you really going to make me wear that?"

A lot had changed since I first met my forever mommy. I wasn't as spunky as I used to be. My legs were wobbly and it was difficult for me to walk. I didn't play with my squirrel friends anymore and I couldn't chase the tennis ball. My body had been changing but the love that I felt from my mommy remained the same. In fact, it felt even more powerful. Mommy and Grandma Jerrie would bring my water dish to where I was resting on my blanket. They did the same with my food bowl. It was like being

served breakfast in bed but with all 3 meals of the day. My mommy cried a lot.

"He's in an incredible amount of pain," I heard the vet say.

I wanted so badly to cuddle with my mommy in bed, like we used to. I wanted to run around with Lola and Jordie. I wanted to help Grandpa Joe fix things. I was secretly wishing he could fix me. I felt broken, like my chew toy.

I remembered the way that Mommy Cindy cried the day that I left, but this was way worse. Ann-Marie was sobbing uncontrollably and I knew why. She was kissing my nose and gently stroking my cheeks. Grandma Jerrie was softly patting my little round head. She was crying, too. Aunt Teresa came over to see me. So did Grandpa Joe, Grandma Mary, and Anthony. I knew this was serious.

"I don't think I will ever find another doggie like you," I heard my mommy say as I drifted off to sleep.

I was hoping she could somehow read my mind. Maybe Grandma Jerrie could. After all, when I was missing my brothers and really wanted a doggie to play with, Grandma Jerrie seemed to know that and had set up a

play date for me. Perhaps at this moment, she could read my mind and tell my mommy what I wanted her to know.

"Mommy, I know you are sad. I don't want to leave you, but it is my time to go. Now, it's your time to open up your heart and your home to other doggies in need. There are so many dogs, especially senior dogs, that are in desperate need of a home like this one. Please don't stop with me. Your love for me must carry on," I barked. I had very little energy and the sounds that I made were faint, but I still barked.

I think she must have understood. I could hear her words faintly. They seemed far away now, but I could still hear them.

"You'll live on forever, my Perfect. I will rescue more senior doggies as a tribute to you."

Remembering Mickey

Ann-Marie and Teresa LaGaipa, identical twin sisters, were born and raised along the Jersey Shore in New Jersey. After teaching in New Jersey for over a decade, they moved to sunny Florida to continue their careers in education. Ann-Marie has been teaching elementary school for 17 years and Teresa has been teaching for 14 years, each year educating young children in the same district and sometimes in the very same school!

The twins decided to combine their love of animals and children with their love for writing and teaching. In this heartfelt Rescue Series, Ann-Marie and Teresa capture their young audiences by sharing their experiences of rescuing animals in need. They hope to inspire others to do the same.

In each story, you'll fall in love with every rescue, just as they have, and you'll emBARK on the adventures together. You'll overcome hurdles and you'll feel the joy that each animal brings, making the house feel like a home.

With each book that you purchase, a percentage of the proceeds will be donated to local rescue shelters. Thank you, in advance, for helping to make a difference in the lives of these special furry friends. You'll also discover that sometimes people think they are saving their new pet, but oftentimes it's the humans that are being rescued.

What You Need To Know Before Adopting

Across

4 Best place to adopt a dog

6 Doggie beauty parlor

11 Pet doctor

12 This protects dogs from rabies and other illnesses

13 A must-have to walk your dog

Down

1 Play things for dogs

2 Throw this for a fun game of fetch

3 As important to give a pet as food and water, often at first sight

5 Walking, chasing balls, and playing with toys are how dogs get this and stay healthy

7 Term used for older dogs

8 State registration or another word for dog's tags

9 Better than a collar to attach a leash, fits around the dog's chest

10 Important to keep clean and available, often in bowl next to food

What every shelter animal wants is a loving home!

Did you know that shelters love volunteers who come spend time with the animals? Ask your mom, dad, or grandparents if your family can spend some time being a fur-buddy's friend!